LANGUAGE ARTS

THE CENTER FOR GIFTED EDUCATION

COLLEGE OF WILLIAM & MARY

D1244887

Beyond Words

Student GRADES 1-2 Guide

Kendall Hunt
publishing company

Cover and title page image © 2011, Shutterstock, Inc.

Kendall Hunt
publishing company

www.kendallhunt.com
Send all inquiries to:
4050 Westmark Drive
Dubuque, IA 52004-1840
1-800-542-6657

Center for Gifted Education
College of William & Mary
PO Box 8795
Williamsburg, VA 23187-8795
757-221-2362
www.cfge.wm.edu

Funded by the Jacob K. Javits Program, United States Department of Education, under a subcontract
from the Washington-Saratoga-Warren-Hamilton-Essex BOCES, Saratoga Springs, New York.

Copyright © 2003, 2011 by Center for Gifted Education

ISBN 978-0-7575-6608-0

Kendall Hunt Publishing Company has the exclusive rights to reproduce this work, to prepare derivative
works from this work, to publicly distribute this work, to publicly perform this work and to publicly
display this work.

All rights reserved. No part of this publication may be reproduced,
stored in a retrieval system, or transmitted, in any form or by any means,
electronic, mechanical, photocopying, recording, or otherwise, without
the prior written permission of Kendall Hunt Publishing Company.

Printed in the United States of America

1 2 3 4 5 6 7 8 9 10 15 14 13 12 11 10

Production Date: May 17, 2010
Printed by: Hess Printing Solutions
Woodstock, IL
United States of America
Batch number: 426608-01

Contents

Letter to Student

Dear Student:

You and your class will be taking part in a special language arts unit called *Beyond Words*. It will help you explore the concept of change. There will be many activities to help you understand this concept. You will also look for figurative language in stories and poems.

Many different kinds of literature will help you explore the concept of change. In class, we will read and discuss poetry and picture books. You will also read one chapter book. We will do listening, vocabulary, and research activities. You will keep a journal to record your thoughts and to get ready for assignments. As you read the literature, you will respond to it and think about its important ideas, images, and words.

The purpose of this book is to provide you with some materials that you will need for the unit. There are many poems in this book, as well as Activity Pages related to what you read and learn.

During this unit, you will use several teaching models. They include:

1. The Literature Web Model
2. The Metaphor Analysis Model
3. The Vocabulary Web Model
4. The Hamburger Model for Persuasive Writing
5. The Writing Process Model

Your teacher will explain how these models work and how you can use them as you read the unit literature and complete the activities.

Sincerely,

Curriculum Development Team
Center for Gifted Education at The College of
William and Mary

Glossary of Literary Terms

The following terms may be useful in discussing the unit readings:

Alliteration: a pattern of sound made by repeating consonant sounds at the beginning of words or inside the words. (Example: softly slipping on slimy stones)

Character: a person in a play or novel.

Climax: the most exciting part of a story or play, usually happening near the end.

Dialogue: the conversation between characters in a play or story.

Figurative language: the use of analogies, metaphors, or similes that describe something by comparing it to something else.

Free verse: verse in which the meter and line length vary and which has no rhyme pattern.

Imagery: words or phrases that help a reader to see characters, scenes, or events in his or her imagination.

Metaphor: a type of figurative language which compares two things by saying one is the other. (Example: The girl is a ray of sunshine.)

Motivation: the reasons or desires that cause a character in a story to act.

Narrator: the speaker or voice that tells a story.

Plot: the series of events in a story.

Point of view: the position from which a narrator tells a story, either within the story (first person) or as an outside observer (third person).

Protagonist: the main character.

Repetition: the repeating of a word or a pattern for a special reason.

Setting: the time and place in which a story happens.

Simile: a type of figurative language in which two things are compared using the words like or as. (Example: Her mind was as sharp as a blade.)

Stanza: a group of lines of verse within a song or poem.

Symbol: an image, word, or object that stands for something else; the image is usually visible, but what it stands for is often invisible. For example, the flag is a symbol of patriotism.

Voice: the perspective of the narrator of the story.

Models

The Literature Web Model

The Literature Web is a model that can help you understand what you read. It encourages you to connect your personal responses with the text. You may complete the web on your own or with a group or whole class. Note the following kinds of ideas in each of the four parts of the web:

Key Words: interesting, unfamiliar, or important words and phrases in the text

Feelings: the reader's feelings and the parts of the text that inspired him/her; the characters' feelings; and the feelings the author may have hoped to inspire in the reader

Ideas: major themes and main ideas of the text; key concepts

Images or Symbols: important images in the text; "pictures" in the reader's mind and the text that inspired them; symbols for bigger ideas

Literature Web Model

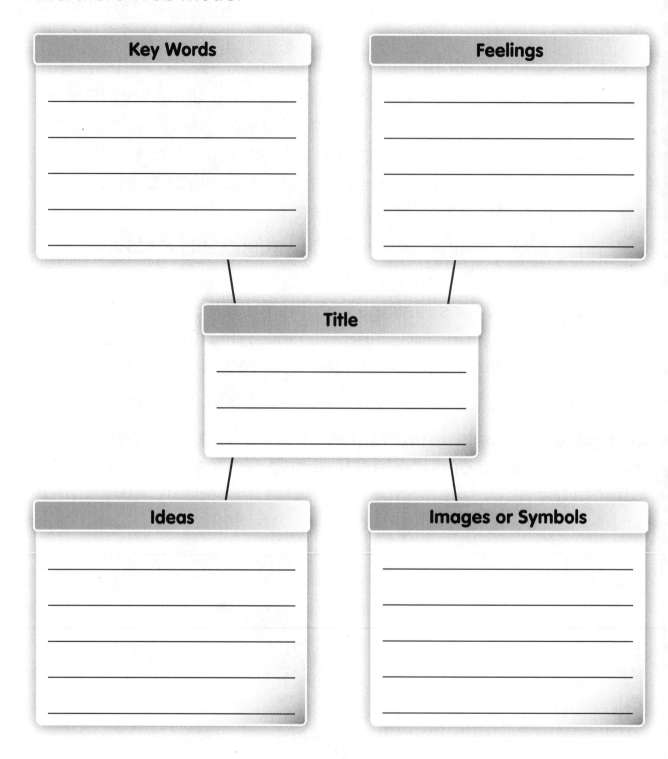

Key Words

_____

_____

_____

_____

Feelings

_____

_____

_____

_____

Title

_____

_____

_____

Ideas

_____

_____

_____

_____

Images or Symbols

_____

_____

_____

_____

Metaphor Analysis Model

A metaphor is a type of figurative language that compares two things by saying one is the other. For example, you might say that your friend's smile is a rainbow, or that your bunny's tail is a cotton ball.

A metaphor has three parts:

- The *topic* is what the comparison is mainly about.
- The *vehicle* is the thing to which the topic is compared.
- The *ground* is how the topic and vehicle are alike. It tells what characteristics they share.

In the first poem in this book, "Fog" by Carl Sandburg, the *topic* is the fog, the *vehicle* is a cat, and the *ground* is movement that seems quiet and sneaky.

This is the Comparison Chart. The three sections show the topic, vehicle, and ground of the comparison. You can use this chart to explore the parts of any metaphor.

Topic of the Comparison	What It Is Compared To	Important Characteristics

The Vocabulary Web Model

The Vocabulary Web is a tool for exploring words. Find the definition of the word and its part of speech, synonyms and antonyms, word stems, and origin. Then try to find at least three other members of the same word family that use one or more of your word's stems. Create a sentence, analogy, picture, or diagram that illustrates your word. Use the Vocabulary Web to organize your responses.

Vocabulary Web Model

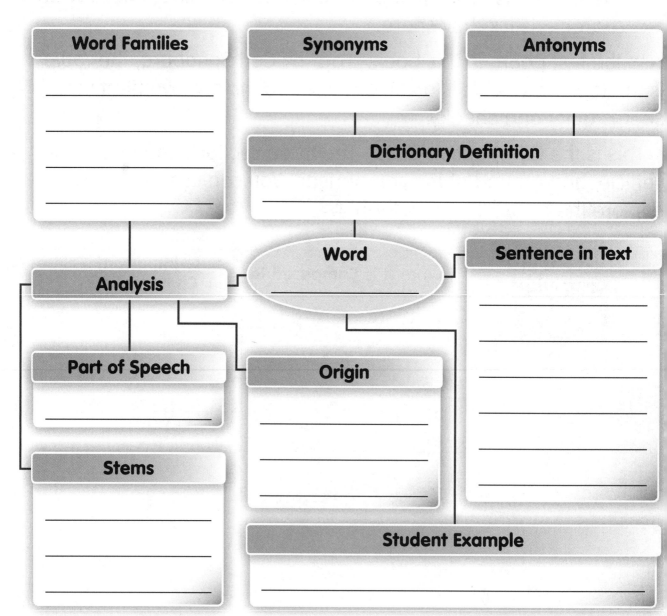

Unit vocabulary words you may want to explore include:

Unit Focus:

metaphor

From "Fog":

harbor

haunches

From "Cobbler, Cobbler":

cobbler

stitch

crown

From "The Moon Has a Face":

thieves

harbor

quays

forks

From "The Moon's the North Wind's Cooky":

cooky

crumble

kneads

greedy

From *Owl Moon:*

journey

bog

shadow

trembling

unfolding

fern

welcomes

From "Daisies":

innocent

daisies

blades

From "April Rain Song":

silver

liquid

lullaby

gutter

From *Frindle*:

tropical

jolt

crimson

reputation

acquire

essential

frantically

procedures

sidetrack

origin

complex

profound

jumble

glanced

reputation

absorbed

oath

blurted

emphasize

forbidding

rebellion

vandalism

prank

fad

mastermind

awkward

preliminary

disruption

ruckus

mania

rascal

remarkable

commotion

villain

endures

oblong

pupil

engraved

The Hamburger Model for Persuasive Writing

The Hamburger Model compares writing a paragraph or essay with making a sandwich. You begin by stating your point of view (the top bun). You then provide at least three reasons for your point of view (the "patties"). A concluding sentence or paragraph closes the piece of writing (the bottom bun).

Hamburger Model for Persuasive Writing

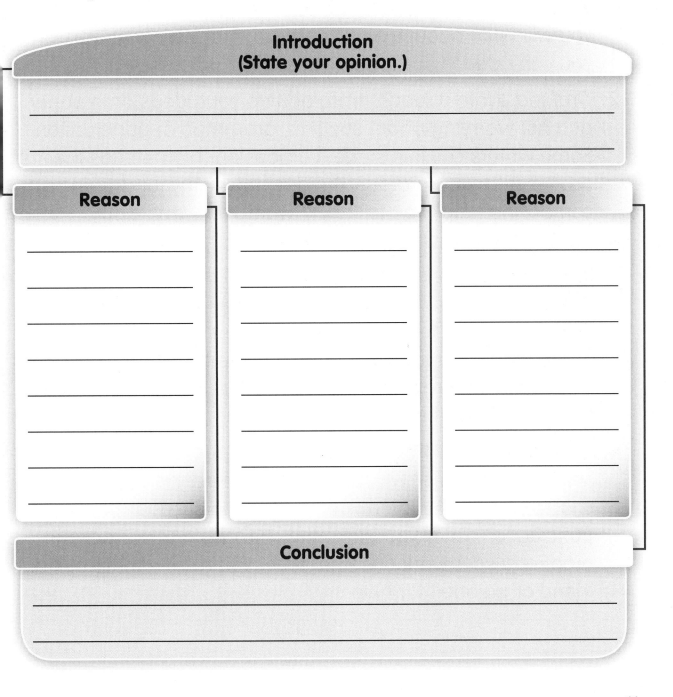

The Writing Process Model

The writing process describes the stages that writers go through to create a piece of writing. The Writing Process Model is used throughout the unit to help you improve your writing.

The following are the stages of the writing process:

1. *Prewriting:* List your ideas and begin to organize them. You may want to use a graphic organizer such as a web or a Venn diagram. Graphic organizers help you to "see" what you will write about in your paragraph or essay. As you write, you can add to your graphic organizer or change it.

2. *Drafting:* Write a rough draft, getting your ideas onto paper and not worrying about spelling, grammar, or punctuation. Some writers call this stage "composing." Sometimes the first draft is a "messing around" stage in which your drafting or composing helps you to "hear" what you want to say.

3. *Revising:* Ask people (friends, family, teachers) to read and listen to your work and to tell you what they like, what they'd like to know more about, and what they don't understand. This is the place to make major changes in your draft. Sometimes you may want to go back to the prewriting stage and redo your graphic organizer so that your paper has a new structure.

4. *Editing:* After you have revised your paper, look for the small changes that will make a big difference. Check your choice of words and look for errors in spelling, grammar, or punctuation. After you make the changes and corrections, proofread your work one final time. You may want to ask a friend or an adult for help.

5. *Sharing or publishing:* There are many ways to share and to publish your work. You can bind it into a book, copy it in your best handwriting and post it on a bulletin board, read it aloud to your class or family, or make it into a gift for someone special.

Fog

Carl Sandburg

The fog comes
on little cat feet.

It sits looking
over harbor and city
on silent haunches
and then moves on.

From *Chicago Poems* by Carl Sandburg. Henry Holt and Company, 1916.

Name: _____ Date: _____

Examples of Change

Directions: Complete the boxes. Write or draw examples of each kind of change.

A change that happens fast	A change that takes a long time

A positive change	A negative change

A change that people cause

A change that happens naturally

A change you expect

A change you do not expect

A neat change

A messy change

Name: _____ Date: _____

Explore Changes in the Weather

Directions: Complete the chart. Write the high and low temperatures every day for five days. Draw a picture showing the weather each day. Then write the generalizations that tell about the changes you saw in the weather over the five-day period.

Day	High Temperature	Low Temperature	Picture of the Weather

Generalizations:

_____

_____

_____

_____

_____

_____

_____

_____

_____

_____

_____

_____

Cobbler, Cobbler

Cobbler, cobbler, mend my shoe,
Have it done by half past two.
Stitch it up and stitch it down,
And I'll give you half a crown.

Mother Goose rhyme

Name: _____ Date: _____

 **Activity**
3A

Rewrite "Cobbler, Cobbler"

Directions: Rewrite each line of "Cobbler, Cobbler." Use words that people use today. You do not need to rhyme.

Cobbler, cobbler, mend my shoe,

Your version: _____

_____

Have it done by half past two.

Your version: _____

_____

Stitch it up and stitch it down,

Your version: _____

_____

And I'll give you half a crown.

Your version: _____

_____

Name: _____ Date: _____

Unit Project

Language changes as people grow and learn, as they move from place to place, or as they give names to new inventions. Language also makes changes happen, as people learn, think, and feel new things because of what they hear or read.

Directions: Find out about language and change in your family. Find answers to these questions. Keep the answers in a notebook or on an audio recorder. You will report your findings later in the unit.

- **Changes to your language**
  How has your language changed as you have grown? What are some words you used for things when you were younger and couldn't say their real names? What are some words you have learned since you started school?

- **Changes to the language of your parents and grandparents**
  How has language changed for your parents and grandparents? What are some words they used when they were your age that people do not usually use now? What are some words they have had to learn for new inventions? (Hint: Ask about computer words!)

- **Changes to language because of moving**
  How has language changed for your family as they have moved from place to place? Have any members of your

family lived in a different state or country? If so, what are some words they used in those other places that they do not use now?

- **Changes caused by language**
  How has language caused change in your family? Find out if any members of your family have had an experience with language that changed them. For example, special words in a poem or song might have changed them. A story might have helped them to change or make a decision.

List the people whom you can ask these questions:

_____

_____

_____

_____

_____

_____

_____

_____

Name: _____ Date: _____

Words for Describing

Directions: In the first column, list some words that tell how things look. In the second column, list words that tell how things sound. In the third column, list words that tell how things feel. Use the examples to get you started.

How Things Look	How Things Sound	How Things Feel
blue bright	loud silent	rough cold

Name: _____ Date: _____

Nouns That Adjectives Could Describe

Directions: Write your adjectives at the top of the chart. Then list nouns that each adjective could describe.

Adjective:	Adjective:	Adjective:
Nouns:	**Nouns:**	**Nouns:**

Name: _____ Date: _____

Activity 4B

Describing Fog and Cats

Directions: List words that describe fog in the left column. List words that describe cats in the right column. When you are finished, find words on the two lists that are alike. Circle them and draw a line connecting them.

Words That Describe Fog	Words That Describe Cats

Name: _____ Date: _____

Comparison Chart

Directions: Use this chart to compare different things that are alike in some way.

Topic of the Comparison	What the Topic Is Compared To	Important Characteristics

Moon Poems

(Robert Louis Stevenson, Vachel Lindsay, and Emily Dickinson)

The moon has a face like the clock in the hall;
She shines on thieves on the garden wall,
On streets and fields and harbor quays,
And birdies asleep in the forks of the trees.

—Robert Louis Stevenson

Robert Louis Stevenson, 1850–1894.

The Moon's the North Wind's cooky.
He bites it, day by day,
Until there's but a rim of scraps
That crumble all away.

The South Wind is a baker.
He kneads clouds in his den,
And bakes a crisp new moon that … greedy
North … Wind … eats … again!

—Vachel Lindsay

Vachel Lindsay, 1879–1931.

The moon was but a chin of gold
A night or two ago,
And now she turns her perfect face
Upon the world below.

—Emily Dickinson

Emily Dickinson, 1830–1886.

Name: _____ Date: _____

 **Activity**
5A

Moon Poem Study

Directions: Answer the questions.

Which poem did you read?

_____

What object does the poet say is like the moon?

_____

What are some words that could describe this object?

_____

_____

_____

Which of these words could also describe the moon?

_____

_____

_____

What does the poet want readers to think or feel about
the moon?

_____

_____

_____

What shape is the moon in your poem? Draw it. Explain how
you knew what shape to draw.

_____

_____

_____

Name: _____ Date: _____

Activity 5B

Moon Chart

Directions: Write in the number the days of the month on the calendar. Look at the moon each night or day. Draw the shape of the moon that you see for each day you see it.

Sunday	Monday	Tuesday	Wednesday	Thursday	Friday	Saturday

Dream Maker

Jane Yolen

The shining silver moon
Is a coin hung in the sky
To pay the old Dream Maker
Whenever he goes by.

Copyright © 1993 by Jane Yolen. First appeared in *What Rhymes with Moon?*, published by Philomel, A Division of Penguin Putnam, Inc. Reprinted by permission of Curtis Brown, Ltd.

Name: _____ Date: _____

Comparisons

Directions: Circle the choice that describes each comparison. If the comparison is a simile or metaphor, write how the two objects are alike.

The sand on the beach looked like dirt.

    simile   metaphor   literal

_____

_____

The wind was a whisper.

    simile   metaphor   literal

_____

_____

The brook babbled like a classroom of excited children.

    simile   metaphor   literal

_____

_____

The river roared like a waterfall.

simile   metaphor   literal

_____

_____

The cub is a little lion.

simile   metaphor   literal

_____

_____

The soldier was as brave as a lion.

simile   metaphor   literal

_____

_____

Name: _____ Date: _____

 **Activity**
6B

Directions: Complete the Literature Web for "Dream Maker."

Key Words	Feelings
_____	_____
_____	_____
_____	_____
_____	_____

Title

_____

_____

_____

Ideas	Images or Symbols
_____	_____
_____	_____
_____	_____
_____	_____

Beyond Words · Lesson 6 · More About Metaphor

Name: _____ Date: _____

What's Like the Sun?

Directions: Write three characteristics of the sun at the top of the chart. Then list other objects with the same characteristic.

Characteristic:	Characteristic:	Characteristic:
Other objects with this characteristic:	**Other objects with this characteristic:**	**Other objects with this characteristic:**

Name: _____ Date: _____

Similes and Metaphors About the Sun

Directions: Write similes and metaphors about the sun. Use your list of objects on Activity 6C to help you.

The sun is like _____

_____

The sun is like _____

_____

The sun is as _____

_____

The sun is as _____

_____

The sun is _____

_____

The sun is _____

_____

Name: _____ Date: _____

Activity 7B

Color Palette

Directions: Choose the best color names from your list. Color in the palette with your colors. Write the names under each color.

Name: _____ Date: _____

Making Comparisons

Directions: Complete the comparisons.

1. as tall as _____

2. as strong as _____

3. as quiet as _____

4. as soft as _____

5. as hard as _____

6. as small as _____

7. as happy as _____

8. as mad as _____

9. as beautiful as _____

10. as bright as _____

Name: _____ Date: _____

Context Clues

Directions: Complete the chart. List the yellow words from *Baloney (Henry P.)* Write what you think each word means. Use context clues. Then look at the last page of the book. Write what each word really means.

Yellow Words	Meaning Based on Context Clues	Real Meaning

Yellow Words	Meaning Based on Context Clues	Real Meaning

Name: _____ Date: _____

Literature Web

Directions: Complete the Literature Web for "Avalanche."

Key Words
_____
_____
_____
_____

Feelings
_____
_____
_____
_____

Title
_____
_____

Ideas
_____
_____
_____
_____

Images or Symbols
_____
_____
_____
_____

Name: _____ Date: _____

 **Activity**
8C

Vocabulary Web

Directions: Complete the Vocabulary Web for the word "avalanche."

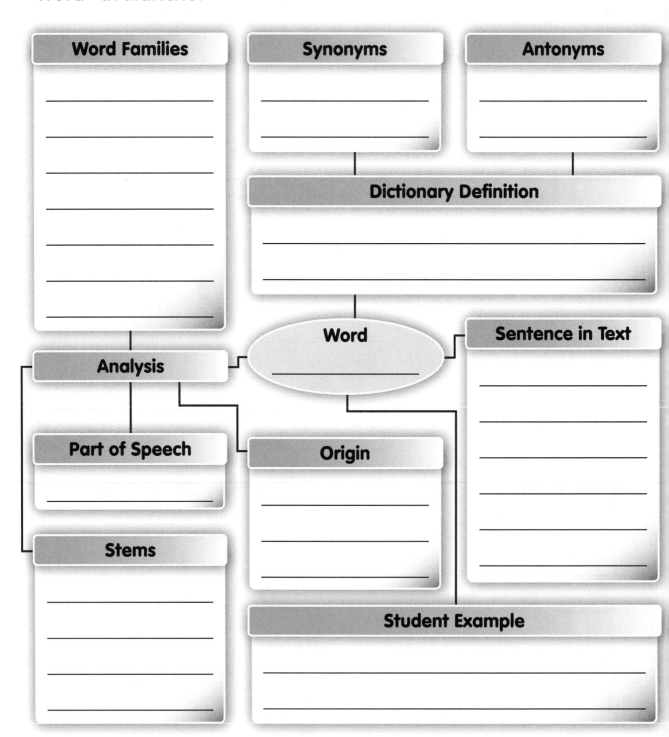

Word Families

Synonyms

Antonyms

Dictionary Definition

Word

Analysis

Sentence in Text

Part of Speech

Origin

Stems

Student Example

Name: _____ Date: _____

Be Still and Listen ...

Directions: Close your eyes, sit quietly, and listen. Your teacher will tell you to open your eyes. Then respond to each sentence.

Write words or a sentence about what you heard or felt.

Draw about what you heard or felt.

Name: _____ Date: _____

 **Activity**
9B

Directions: Complete the Literature Web for *Owl Moon.*

Key Words
_____
_____
_____
_____

Feelings
_____
_____
_____
_____

Title
_____
_____
_____

Ideas
_____
_____
_____
_____

Images or Symbols
_____
_____
_____
_____

Name: _____ Date: _____

From Nervous to Brave

Directions: Think about a time you felt nervous about doing something but felt brave afterward. Then respond to each sentence.

Write words or sentences about the time that you felt nervous about doing something but felt brave afterward.
Draw a picture about that time.

Name: _____ Date: _____

 **Activity**
9D

Life Changes

Directions: Complete the chart. List changes that happened in your life from preschool to kindergarten. List changes that happened in your life from kindergarten until now. List the good changes in the "Positive" column. List the bad changes in the "Negative" column.

	Positive	Negative
From preschool to kindergarten		
From kindergarten until now		

Name: _____ Date: _____

The Hamburger Model
for Persuasive Writing

Introduction
(State your opinion.)

_____

_____

Reason	**Reason**	**Reason**

Conclusion

_____

_____

Name: _____ Date: _____

Activity 10B

Moving

Directions: Read the paragraph. Then circle the introduction in green. Circle the reasons in blue. Circle the conclusion in red.

Moving is a positive kind of change. When you move to a

new home, you get a new room. You can decorate it. You can

try different ways to set up your things in the room. When

you move, you also get to go to a new school. You can meet

new friends there. Also, in a new place, you can visit places

that you've never visited before. You can visit new parks

and stores. These are the reasons why I think moving is an

exciting and positive change.

Name: _____ Date: _____

Jumbled Paragraph

Directions: Cut out each sentence strip. Put the sentences in the best order. Use the Hamburger Model to help you.

- -

Finally, you have to leave your friends behind.

- -

Also, you have to pack up your things and maybe throw some of them away.

- -

Moving is a negative change in many ways.

- -

These are the reasons why I think moving is a sad and negative change.

- -

First, you have to get used to a new place, including a school where you do not know anybody.

Name: _____ Date: _____

The Hamburger Model
for Persuasive Writing

Directions: Choose an issue that matters to you. Complete the Hamburger Model with information about your opinion on the issue. Also give your reasons for your opinion. Write a conclusion that sums up your ideas.

Introduction
(State your opinion.)

_____

_____

Reason	**Reason**	**Reason**
_____	_____	_____
_____	_____	_____
_____	_____	_____
_____	_____	_____
_____	_____	_____
_____	_____	_____
_____	_____	_____
_____	_____	_____

Conclusion

_____

_____

Daisies

Christina Rossetti

Where innocent bright-eyed daisies are,
With blades of grass between,
Each daisy stands up like a star
Out of a sky of green.

From *Rainbow in the Sky,* Harcourt Brace & Company.

Name: _____ Date: _____

Activity
11A

Peer Review of Writing

Directions: Read your partner's Hamburger Model. Write a check mark next to the answer to each question. Then complete the sentence at the end.

1. Does the introduction give the opinion?

_____ The introduction gives the opinion clearly.

_____ The introduction gives the opinion somewhat clearly.

_____ The introduction does not give the opinion.

2. Do the reasons support the opinion?

_____ All the reasons support the opinion.

_____ Some of the reasons support the opinion.

_____ The reasons do not support the opinion.

3. Are the reasons strong?

_____ All the reasons are strong.

_____ Some of the reasons are strong.

_____ The reasons are not strong.

4. Does the conclusion sum up the ideas?

_____ The conclusion sums up the ideas clearly.

_____ The conclusion sums up the ideas somewhat clearly.

_____ The conclusion does not sum up the ideas.

These are ways to make the model better:

_____

_____

_____

_____

_____

_____

_____

_____

_____

_____

_____

Name: _____ Date: _____

 **Activity**
11B

Directions: Complete the Literature Web for "Daisies."

Key Words	Feelings
_____	_____
_____	_____
_____	_____
_____	_____

Title

_____

_____

_____

Ideas	Images or Symbols
_____	_____
_____	_____
_____	_____
_____	_____

Name: _____ Date: _____

Making Analogies

Directions: Complete each analogy.

1. Daisies are to the grass as stars are to _____.

2. Day is to the sun as night is to _____.

3. Bird is to nest as _____ is to _____.

4. Attacker is to castle as germ is to _____.

5. Swimming is to summer as ice skating is to _____.

6. Red is to apple as _____ is to _____.

7. Lion is to cub as _____ is to _____.

8. Moon is to Earth as Earth is to _____.

9. Painting is to canvas as sunset is to _____.

10. Foot is to shoe as hand is to _____.

Write your own analogy!

_____ is to _____

as _____ is to _____.

Name: _____ Date: _____

Homonym Sentences

Directions: Write sentences using homonym pairs. Draw a picture for each sentence.

1. _____

_____

2. _____

_____

Name: _____ Date: _____

Activity 12B

Homophone Sentences

Directions: Write sentences using homophone pairs. Draw a picture for each sentence.

1. _____

   _____

2. _____

   _____

Name: _____ Date: _____

The Hamburger Model for Persuasive Writing

Directions: Plan a paragraph about your favorite season. Use the Hamburger Model to help plan the paragraph.

Introduction
(State your opinion.)

_____

_____

Reason	**Reason**	**Reason**
_____	_____	_____

Conclusion

_____

_____

Name: _____ Date: _____

Peer Review of Writing

Directions: Read your partner's paragraph. Write a check mark next to the answer to each question. Then complete the two sentences at the end.

1. Does the introduction give the opinion?

_____ The introduction gives the opinion clearly.

_____ The introduction gives the opinion somewhat clearly.

_____ The introduction does not give the opinion.

2. Do the reasons support the opinion?

_____ All the reasons support the opinion.

_____ Some of the reasons support the opinion.

_____ The reasons do not support the opinion.

3. Are the reasons strong?

_____ All the reasons are strong.

_____ Some of the reasons are strong.

_____ The reasons are not strong.

4. Does the conclusion sum up the ideas?

_____ The conclusion sums up the ideas clearly.

_____ The conclusion sums up the ideas somewhat clearly.

_____ The conclusion does not sum up the ideas.

The writing is strong in these ways:

_____

_____

_____

These are ways to make the writing better:

_____

_____

_____

Name: _____ Date: _____

Haiku Structure

Directions: Read each haiku. Write a slash "/" between the syllables in each word. Count the syllables in each line. Write the number of syllables in the boxes.

☐ The birch leaves flutter,

☐ Their edges turning yellow—

☐ Autumn almost here.

☐ Little shoots of green

☐ Raise their hands shyly to ask,

☐ Winter over yet?

Name: _____ Date: _____

Literature Web

Directions: Complete the Literature Web for "Autumn."

Key Words
_____
_____
_____
_____

Feelings
_____
_____
_____
_____

Title
_____
_____
_____

Ideas
_____
_____
_____
_____

Images or Symbols
_____
_____
_____
_____

Name: _____ Date: _____

 **Activity 14B**

Personification Identification

Directions: Circle the item that is acting like a person in each sentence. Write the action that the item is doing.

The wind sang a happy song as it scattered the leaves on the street.

ACTION: _____

The daisies nodded their heads at the passersby.

ACTION: _____

The mist kissed the baby's cheeks.

ACTION: _____

The snow whispered cool secrets in my ear as it began to fall.

ACTION: _____

The stars winked at me before I fell asleep.

ACTION: _____

Name: _____ Date: _____

Personification Poem

Directions: List characteristics of the seasons in each column on the chart. Choose one of the seasons. Write sentences that personify the season. Then write a poem about the season using personification. Write your sentences and poem on another sheet of paper.

Winter	Spring	Summer

We will write a poem about the season of _____.

1. _____

_____

_____

_____

_____

2 _____

_____

_____

_____

_____

3. _____

_____

_____

_____

_____

Name: _____ Date: _____

Literature Web

Directions: Complete the Literature Web for *Follow the Drinking Gourd.*

Key Words	Feelings
_____	_____
_____	_____
_____	_____
_____	_____

Title

_____
_____
_____

Ideas	Images or Symbols
_____	_____
_____	_____
_____	_____
_____	_____

Name: _____ Date: _____

 **Activity**
15B

Literature Web

Directions: Complete the Literature Web for *Sweet Clara and the Freedom Quilt.*

Key Words
_____
_____
_____
_____

Feelings
_____
_____
_____
_____

Title
_____
_____
_____

Ideas
_____
_____
_____
_____

Images or Symbols
_____
_____
_____
_____

Name: _____ Date: _____

Life as a Journey

Directions: Listen to your classmates' sentences. Complete the boxes with words that tell about travel and can also tell about life.

Words About the Path or Road

Words About Things That Happen on a Journey

Other Words

**Activity
16B**

Literature Web

Directions: Complete the Literature Web for *Flotsam.*

Key Words	Feelings
_____	_____
_____	_____
_____	_____
_____	_____

Title
_____
_____
_____

Ideas	Images or Symbols
_____	_____
_____	_____
_____	_____
_____	_____

Name: _____ Date: _____

Change Chart

Directions: Complete the boxes. Write or draw examples of each kind of change in your life journey.

A change that happened fast	A change that took a long time

A positive change	A negative change

A change that people caused	A change that happened naturally

A change you expected	A change you did not expect

Name: _____ Date: _____

Literature Web

Directions: Complete the Literature Web for Chapter 9 of *Frindle*.

Key Words	Feelings
_____	_____
_____	_____
_____	_____
_____	_____
_____	_____

Title

_____
_____
_____

Ideas	Images or Symbols
_____	_____
_____	_____
_____	_____
_____	_____

Name: _____ Date: _____

 **Activity**
17B

A Title for One of Harris Burdick's Mysteries

Directions: Answer the questions.

What do you see in the picture?

_____

_____

_____

_____

What title would you give the picture?

_____

_____

What would be the topic of a story with this picture and title be about?

_____

_____

_____

_____

Name: _____ Date: _____

The Hamburger Model
for Persuasive Writing

Directions: Do you think that all students in your grade should read *Flotsam* by David Wiesner? Why or why not? Complete the Hamburger Model with your opinion, reasons , and a conclusion.

Introduction
(State your opinion.)

_____

_____

Reason	**Reason**	**Reason**

Conclusion

_____

_____

Name: _____ Date: _____

Write a Concrete Poem

Directions: Write the title of your poem. Then draw a light pencil outline of the object which is the topic of your poem. Then write your poem around or inside the outline.

Title: _____

Name: _____ Date: _____

Change Chart

Directions: Complete the boxes. Write or draw examples of each kind of change from your research or your classmates' research.

A change that happens fast	A change that takes a long time

A positive change	A negative change

A change that people cause	A change that happens naturally

A change you expect	A change you do not expect

April Rain Song

Langston Hughes

Let the rain kiss you.
Let the rain beat upon your head with silver liquid drops.
Let the rain sing you a lullaby.

The rain makes still pools on the sidewalk.
The rain makes running pools in the gutter.
The rain plays a little sleep-song on our roof at night—

And I love the rain.

From *The Collected Poems of Langston Hughes* by Langston Hughes, copyright © 1994 by The Estate of Langston Hughes. Used by permission of Alfred A. Knopf, a division of Random House, Inc.

Name: _____ Date: _____

Activity
20A

Change Chart

Directions: Complete the boxes. Write or draw an example of each kind of change from *Frindle*.

A change that happened fast	A change that took a long time

A positive change	A negative change

A change that people caused	A change that happened naturally

A change you expected	A change you did not expect